DISCOVERING PAINTINGS

OUT & ABOUT

Anne Civardi

Chrysalis Children's Books
in association with The National Gallery, London

First published in the UK in 2003 by

Chrysalis Children's Books
The Chrysalis Building
Bramley Road
London W10 6SP

© [This edition] Chrysalis Children's Books
Text © Anne Civardi & Ruth Thomson 2003
Illustrations © National Gallery Company Limited 2003
From an original idea created by National Gallery Company, 2001,
which was generously supported by Mr and Mrs Anthony Speelman

ISBN 1 84138 955 2

British Library in Publication data for this book is available from the British Library

Editorial manager: Joyce Bentley
Consultant: Erika Langmuir
Educational consultant: Hector Doyle
Design: Mei Lim
Illustrator: Serena Feneziani
Project manager for National Gallery Company: Jan Green

Printed in China

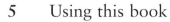
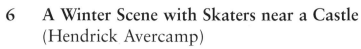

Contents

About this book

The landscape paintings in this book have been chosen because they all explore different scenes in the town or country. Some show real places that the artists knew well and loved, others were painted from the artists' imagination. Often paintings are a mixture of what an artist sees, knows and feels.

John Constable, who painted *The Hay Wain,* for example, grew up and spent much of his life in Suffolk, the part of England shown in *The Hay Wain.* Artists like him took great care about how the scenes of places they loved or enjoyed should look. They made many sketches and drawings outside, which they used back in their studios to paint the final picture. This often took them many months to finish.

The painting *Rain, Steam and Speed* shows how important it was to the artist to create a dramatic atmosphere and feeling of speed and power in his pictures. Turner was very excited by extremes in nature and travelled all over Europe to paint spectacular scenery, blizzards, storms at sea, as well as gorgeous sunrises and sunsets. He is said to have stuck his head out of the window of this very train to experience the thrill of its speed.

By contrast, Renoir's picture, *Boating on the Seine,* is a much more peaceful scene. Like other Impressionist artists, he painted partly in the open air, capturing his impression, or idea, of how things looked at a particular moment. Impressionists were fascinated by light and painted quickly knowing that colours changed endlessly with the light. Renoir especially liked to paint the glittering effect of sunlight on water and people enjoying themselves.

Looking at landscapes

Landscape painters, like most artists, think hard about how to arrange, or compose, a picture, so that your eyes are drawn into the painting, making it interesting and enjoyable to look at. Imagine what it would be like to walk into and wander around each of the landscape paintings in this book. Think about where you might be going. Whom do you meet? Notice the colours. Look at the plants and trees. Is it a calm, windy or rainy day? Do you like being in this place?

Using this book

This book focuses on six main landscape paintings. There are four sections about each picture that will help you to find out more about it.

 asks questions about the painting, which can all be answered by looking at certain details.

 suggests activities that involve your senses and your imagination.

 gives background information about the painting and includes answers to some of the *Look Closer* questions.

 provides another painting on a similar theme for you to compare and contrast with the first one.

A Winter Scene with Skaters near a Castle

(ABOUT 1608 – 9)

Hendrick Avercamp

I n this busy picture, it seems that the whole town is out, chatting,
skating and dancing on the frozen lake. The artist who painted it
is famous for his detailed winter scenes. Although he could not speak
or hear, he must have had very good eyesight, which he used
to observe and paint the people in his town in Holland.

LOOK CLOSER

How do the reflections of the people on the
ice differ from those playing on the snow?

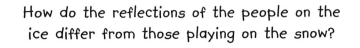

What two things has the artist included
that tell you this picture is set in Holland?
(Clue: they are fluttering in the wind.)

What do you notice about the colours in the foreground
compared with those in the distance?

What kind of building can you see in the background,
half-hidden in the mist to the left of the castle?

How can you tell that it is a freezing cold winter's day?
How do you know the ice is very thick?

TAKE ACTION

The more you look at the picture,
the more you will see.

Can you spot these things?
- two people falling over
- a man helping a woman
  put on her skates
- a big hole in the ice
- a boy throwing a snowball
- the artist's initials

Pretend you are one of the people
in the painting, either rich or poor.
Think about:
- how you got to the lake
- what clothes you are wearing
- whom you came to meet
- what you came to do

Describe one of the people in the picture
and see if a friend can guess who it is.

An Icy Outing

Avercamp used to fill his sketchbooks with coloured drawings of people enjoying themselves on the ice and snow. In this painting, there are over 100 people, from the richest, dressed in their finery, to the poorest peasants.

Fishing boats are stuck in ice so thick that it can support horse-drawn sleighs as well as all those people! The artist's winter scenes look so realistic and detailed that it is hard to imagine this picture is not a real scene, painted outside. In fact, the artist created it in his studio from his sketches and his imagination.

By this time, Holland had just become an independent country. The striped orange, white and blue Dutch flags fluttering in the icy wind probably reminded people of Holland's newly-won freedom. These same colours appear all over the painting – in the people's clothing, in the sky and the ice, as well as in the brick of the buildings. How many people can you see wearing clothes painted these colours?

LOOK FURTHER

A Scene on the Ice near a Town
(ABOUT 1615) **Hendrick Avercamp**

Here is another busy winter scene painted by Avercamp about seven years later than the one on page 6.

There are at least 10 similarities between the two pictures, both set in Holland. Can you spot them all?

What do you think might *be* made in the building on the right?
(Clue: look at the barrels stacked up against the wall.)

In the distance there are some people playing a game called 'Kolf', which is an early form of a game we play now.
What do you think we call it?

Can you spot these things?
• two small dogs
• four chickens
• the Dutch flag
• an axe in a cutting block
• a man putting on his skates
• a woman sitting alone on a chair
• a woman who has fallen over on the ice

The Avenue at Middelharnis

(1689) **Meindert Hobbema**

I n this peaceful landscape, the artist seems to be inviting us
to travel down the long road to a distant village. The tall,
thin poplar trees on either side dominate the painting, seeming
to get smaller and smaller as they get further away. This gives
a feeling of depth and distance, known as *perspective*.

LOOK CLOSER

Apart from the poplar trees, what other things
give us a sense of distance?

Do you think it would take longer to walk from
the first tree to the man with his dog,
or from the dog to the end of the avenue?

Which parts of the land are cultivated and which are wild?
What crops can you see?

What are the people in the picture doing?

How might the ruts in the road have been made?

Where do you think the sun is in the sky?
(Clue: look at the patches of shadow on the ground.)

TAKE ACTION

Imagine you are walking down the
road to the village of Middelharnis.

- Have you travelled a long way?
- Do you have far to go?
- Whom do you meet on the way?
- What might you say to the man
  tending his crop?
- What catches your eye?
- Why are you going to Middelharnis?

Think of a journey you often take –
perhaps to school or to a friend's house.

- Do you walk or go by car, bus or train?
- What is the scenery like on the way?
- Is it in the city or the countryside?
- What kind of surface does
  the road have?
- Is there any building you remember?
- Is the journey exciting or dull?

An Avenue of Trees

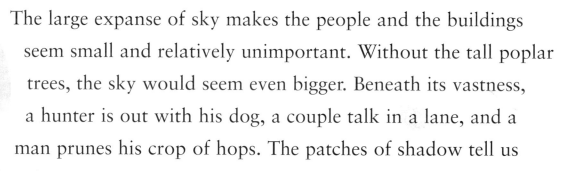

In his picture, Hobbema gives us the feeling of being in the middle of a long journey. To give us a sense of distance, he has not only painted the trees, people and houses smaller and smaller and less detailed along the road, but he has also made the sides of the road diagonal, almost meeting at the horizon. Painters have used diagonal lines to produce an effect of distance for more than 500 years.

The large expanse of sky makes the people and the buildings seem small and relatively unimportant. Without the tall poplar trees, the sky would seem even bigger. Beneath its vastness, a hunter is out with his dog, a couple talk in a lane, and a man prunes his crop of hops. The patches of shadow tell us that the sun is high to the left.

At the time the picture was painted, the Dutch had to work hard to live on their land, which was below the level of the sea. Many canals and ditches needed to be dug to drain the flat, open countryside so that crops could be grown. A painting like this one shows the results of all their efforts.

Avenue at Chantilly
(1888) **Paul Cézanne**

This avenue of trees painted by Paul Cézanne in Chantilly, which is close to Paris in France, is quite different from the one by Hobbema.

You can glimpse only a small patch of blue sky and the trees blend together, dominating the picture. What other differences can you spot?

Do you think this painting is as realistic as Hobbema's?

Imagine walking down this avenue of trees.
• Do you find it peaceful or noisy?
• Is it sunny or shady?
• What do you find at the end of the avenue?

Cézanne has used very few colours in this painting. How many different ones can you spot?

13

The Stonemason's Yard

(ABOUT 1726 – 30) **Canaletto**

This painting by Canaletto is a glimpse into everyday life in the back streets of Venice over 250 years ago. The artist is famous for his detailed pictures of Venice's grandest canals, buildings and festivals. His real name was Giovanni Antonio Canal. Canaletto was his nickname – it means 'Little Canal'.

LOOK CLOSER

Can you find a woman spinning, two stonemasons carving and a woman looking over a balcony? Who else can you see? What are they doing? What animals can you spot?

How can you tell that Venice gets quite hot in the summer?
(Clue: look at the windows.)

Look at how Canaletto has used varying shades of brown to show different materials, such as wood, stone, tiles and cloth.
How many shades of brown can you see?
Which is the darkest and which is the lightest?

What different kinds of building can you see?
What materials are they made from?

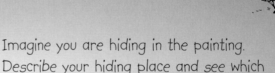

TAKE ACTION

If you stepped into the picture, who or what would you hear making these sounds?
- banging
- shouting
- calling

- crying
- ringing
- talking

Stand in the pose of one of the people in the picture and see if one of your friends can work out who you are.

Imagine you are hiding in the painting. Describe your hiding place and *see* which of your friends can point to it first.

Find three places in sunlight and three places in shadow. Look carefully and *see* if you can work out where the sun is shining from.
(Clue: when you stand in sunlight your body blocks the sun and casts a shadow.)

Venice – City of Canals

Canaletto spent most of his life in Venice, painting views of the city, which he sold to tourists. Venice is unique – its buildings were constructed upon hundreds of flat, muddy islands in a shallow lagoon off the north Italian coast. It has canals instead of roads, so people travel about by boats and gondolas.

Many of the buildings were built from clay bricks, which are lighter and cheaper than stone. Brick churches and palaces were often faced with a layer of carved stone to make them look more magnificent. The stonemasons in the picture are carving stone to face a nearby church, which is out of sight. Can you see a building across the canal faced with stone? This and the brick church next to it are still standing. All the rest of the buildings have been knocked down.

In the picture on page 14, Canaletto has created areas of contrasting light, bright areas with dark, shaded ones nearby. The things that are painted light stand out, while the darker ones are pushed back. Look at the painting with your eyes half-closed and see if you can see some of the areas of light and dark.

LOOK FURTHER

A Regatta on the Grand Canal
(ABOUT 1740) **Canaletto**

This much grander picture of Venice by Canaletto shows a colourful carnival event held every year where men raced each other in their one-oared gondolas.

Although the two pictures are of very different scenes in Venice, you can tell they are by the same artist. What similarities can you spot?

Venice is the only place in the world that uses gondolas for transport.
How many different kinds can you spot?

Can you spot three things that tell you this is a festival?

Where do you think the prizes will be presented to the winners?

Why might it *be* difficult to race a one-oared gondola?

17

The Hay Wain

(1821)

John Constable

I magine you are one of the drivers of this hay cart, or wain. You have just driven it into the water to cool down the horses and allow them to have a refreshing drink. Soon you will help the haymakers in the distant fields load up the wain with big bales of hay.

Constable once wrote a letter which said,
"The sound of water escaping from mill dams, willows,
old rotten planks, slimy posts and brickwork,
I love such things. These scenes made me a painter."
Which of these things can you see in the painting?

How many animals can you spot in the picture?

**Why has Constable painted the trees on the
right-hand side of the picture so much
smaller than the other trees?**

Constable liked to add splashes of red to contrast
with the different shades of green in his paintings.
**Can you glimpse the dog's red tongue?
What other red things do you see?**

**What do you think the woman is doing
in the water near the cottage?**

TAKE ACTION

Pretend you are one of the drivers of the hay wain. Describe to a friend what you did before you reached the river. Think about the journey you might have had.
- **Was it fast or slow?**
- **Did the horses need to stop on the way?**
- **What was the countryside you passed through like?**
- **Was it a comfortable trip?**

Why do you think the dog is such an important part of the painting?
(Clue: look at where it leads your eye.)

Imagine you are standing on the river bank.
Who or what do you think is making the following sounds?
- barking
- rustling
- lapping
- quacking
- whistling
- talking

An English Painting

Constable was renowned for his pictures of the English countryside. *The Hay Wain*, his most famous, shows a view of the River Stour in Suffolk, England. The cottage beside the river belonged to a deaf farmer called Willy Lott, whom the artist had known since he was a boy. Willy lived there all his life.

In the painting, the sun is almost overhead, hidden by billowing clouds that seem to be floating across the summer sky. The fields and water below are mottled with patches of light and shade. Constable has picked out areas of particular brightness with highlights of yellow or white. Notice the thick ridges of colour in the water and on the leaves of the trees and bushes.

At the time, people complained that Constable's highlights looked like snow and that the painting seemed only half-finished. They preferred the smoother, blended brushstrokes of other landscape artists. In fact, John Constable made many sketches before starting on the final painting, which took him several months to finish.

 **LOOK FURTHER**

Salisbury Cathedral from the Meadows
(1831) **John Constable**

Compare *The Hay Wain* with this picture, also by Constable. He made sketches of it while staying with his friend Archdeacon Fisher.

The Archdeacon lived in the house shown on the right, below the end of the rainbow. Can you find five similarities between both paintings?

Compare the light and shade in the two pictures.
How do they differ?

Do you think Constable painted this picture
in the summer or winter?
What kind of weather is it?
How can you tell?

What do you think the small structure under
the trees on the left of the picture is?
(Clue: no-one is living there.)

Why do you think the horses
are standing in the water?

21

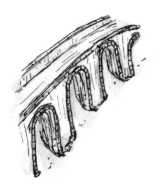

Rain, Steam and Speed

(BEFORE 1844) **J. M. W. Turner**

Imagine what it must have felt like to travel on one of the first steam trains ever invented. In this picture, the artist has tried to capture the excitement and exhilaration people felt at its power and speed. The dark locomotive thunders over a bridge towards us with its headlights flashing.

LOOK CLOSER

How has the artist shown the feeling of speed?

How would you describe the weather?

What other form of transport can you see which
is slower and more old-fashioned than the steam train?

What tells you that this is a steam train?

To help capture the energy and movement, Turner has painted parts of
the picture with swirly brushstrokes of thick paint, known as 'impasto'.
Can you see where the paint is thicker?
Where is it painted more thinly?
Can you see where the paint is swirly?

TAKE ACTION

Look at the painting. Close your eyes
and then open them again.

What is your first impression?
What do you notice in the foreground,
middle and background?

Which of the following words best describe
the mood of the painting?

- gentle
- quiet
- energetic
- dynamic
- noisy
- bright
- explosive
- dull

Imagine you are on the train.
Describe to a friend:

- the noise
- the smells
- the wind and rain
- the sights of the towns
  and countryside rushing by

Where do you think the artist was
standing when he painted this picture?

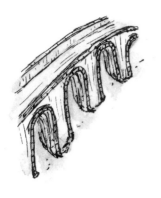

 **READ ABOUT**

A Moving Picture

Turner became known as the 'painter of light' because of his interest in painting the effects of steam, smoke, air and water. In this dramatic picture, he has used swirls and slashes of paint to give the feeling of rain driving across the path of the train, and for the engine's smoke and steam.

As well as the train, Turner has painted some other things in the picture. To the left, you can see two figures in a boat on the water. One appears to be holding a black umbrella, which tells us that it is probably raining. Behind them, you can just glimpse a group of people standing at the water's edge. They seem to be waving as the train hurtles past.

This train ran on the Great Western Railway from London to Bristol. The bridge it is crossing was designed by the famous engineer Isambard Brunel. Stretching across the Thames between Taplow and Maidenhead, it was completed in 1839. There is also a second bridge in the painting. If you look very carefully, you can dimly see the town of Maidenhead in the distant background behind it.

LOOK FURTHER

Compare Turner's action-packed painting with Claude Monet's more calm and peaceful *The Gare St-Lazare*.

Although they both feature steam trains, they are very different. Can you spot at least six differences?

Notice the vertical and horizontal lines in Monet's painting, and diagonal ones in Turner's.
What mood do they suggest to you?

What is the main focus of attention in this picture?

What is happening in the background?

Imagine you are in the station about to board one of these steam trains.
What might you see, hear and do?

- Is it noisy?
- Is it cold?
- Is it rainy?
- Is it dark and gloomy?
- How long have you been waiting?
- Where are you going?

Boating on the Seine

(ABOUT 1879 – 80)

Pierre-Auguste Renoir

Imagine it is a hot, hazy summer's day and you are rowing lazily down the River Seine near Paris, just like these two girls. A slight breeze cools the air, as the sunlight flickers on the water, casting shadows and reflections on its rippling surface.

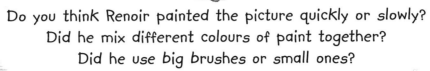

Renoir was fascinated by the way certain colours, such
as yellow and violet, blue and orange, and green and red,
make each other look brighter when painted side by side.
Can you spot two colours in the picture that do this?

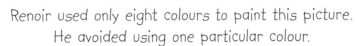

Do you think Renoir painted the picture quickly or slowly?
Did he mix different colours of paint together?
Did he use big brushes or small ones?

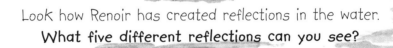

Renoir used only eight colours to paint this picture.
He avoided using one particular colour.
Can you work out which colour this is?
How many of the eight colours can you spot?

Look how Renoir has created reflections in the water.
What five different reflections can you see?

If the picture came to life:
• what five things would be moving?
• what six noises might you hear?

What do you think the two girls might
be saying to each other as they row
down the river?
Think about the weather, the scenery
and the different activities going on
in the painting.

Look carefully at the picture.
**Can you find something made of each
of these materials?**
• cloth   • wood
• metal   • brick
• stone   • glass

Imagine you are an artist painting this
scene on a hot summer's day.
**What different pieces of equipment
do you think you need?**
(Clue: there are at least eight things.)

Flickering Lights

R enoir liked to paint pictures of things he could see with his own eyes rather than stories from the Bible or myths. He was one of a group of painters known as *Impressionists*.

They carefully observed landscapes at different seasons and times of day, and in all weathers, dabbing paint quickly on to their canvases to capture the changing effects of light on outdoor scenes of everyday life.

In the past, artists had to make their own paints but, by the time Renoir started painting, bright colours were available in squeezy, metal tubes. New types of brushes and lightweight, portable easels had also been invented, which made it much easier for artists to paint outside.

Renoir avoided black and used pure, strong colours which he did not mix together. He knew that certain colours looked extra bright when they were painted next to each other, such as the orange of the boat and the blue of the water. If you look closely, you can see the separate strokes of colour beside each other. From a distance they seem to blend together.

 **LOOK FURTHER**

Bathers at La Grenouillère
(1869) **Claude-Oscar Monet**

During the summer of 1869, Renoir painted with his great friend Monet on the banks of the River Seine.

Compare Renoir's picture with this one of Monet's. What are the three main differences between them?

What are the two women on the right of the walkway about to do? How do you know?

What colours has Monet used to give light to different parts of this picture?

How many *kinds of brushstrokes* can you find in this picture?
Which of the following words describe them?
- broad
- fine
- flat
- squiggly
- stumpy
- thick

29

Things to do

Each one of these six activities is related to one of the pictures in this book. Before you start, look back at the painting to help you remember all about it.

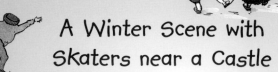

A Winter Scene with Skaters near a Castle

Look carefully at the painting on page 6. Draw the six people in the picture who interest you most. Give everyone a speech bubble. Then write in the bubbles what you imagine each person might be thinking.

The Avenue at Middelharnis

Draw a road with diagonal lines, like the one below, in the centre of a plain piece of paper. Then add three people, some trees, flowers and animals along the road, giving a feeling of distance, or perspective.

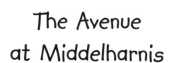

The Stonemason's Yard

Are these statements about the picture of 'The Stonemason's Yard' on page 14 true or false?

1. The stonemasons are carving with saws.
2. All the windows on the houses have shutters.
3. The woman leaning out of the window is airing her bedding.
4. The tall church bell-tower has a cross on the top.
5. The little child on the ground is peeing.
6. None of the gondolas is moving.

The Hay Wain

Write down the missing words that describe the picture on page 18.

The Hay Wain is one of Constable's most famous paintings.
It shows a wooden .... pulled by three ...... standing in a shallow .....
with ..... swimming in it. On the river bank, there is a small ...... ,
which has dirty white walls, a red-tiled roof and a chimney with .....
coming out of it. A ... runs along the bank, watching the hay wain.
On the other side of the river, half-hidden in the ..... is
a fisherman holding a long .... In the distant fields,
bordered by rows of tall ..... men are cutting the ... .

Rain, Steam and Speed

Draw a picture of how you would
show speed – perhaps a rocket, train
or aeroplane, or anything travelling
really fast. Remember curved and
diagonal lines are action lines.

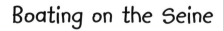

Boating on the Seine

Ask a friend to do this activity with you.
Describe Renoir's painting on page 26,
while your friend turns his or her back and
draws (without peeping) what you are
describing. Then ask your friend
to do the same for you.

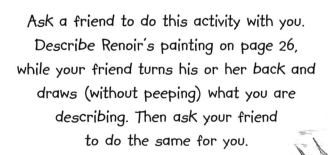

Glossary

background
The area in a painting which seems to be furthest away from the viewer. The opposite of foreground.

compose
The way that an artist arranges everything in a picture – people, objects, shapes and colours.

foreground
The area in a painting which seems to be nearest to the viewer. The opposite of background.

highlight
An area in a painting which seems to attract the most light, and standing out from the shadows, draws the most attention to itself. Highlights are often painted in white.

horizon
The line where the land or sea appears to meet the sky.

Impressionists
A group of painters working in France in the late 19th century. They often worked outdoors, painting things they could see while trying to capture changing effects of light and movement.

landscape
A painting showing an outdoor view of a real or imaginary place.

mood
The overall feeling of a painting – calm, joyous, threatening, angry, etc.

perspective
A method of drawing or painting spaces, figures and objects to make them appear three-dimensional.

sketch
A quick drawing, either of what artists see in front of them, or in preparation for a painting.

Index